teacher's friend publications

W9-BLU-282

Sixth Grade Basic Skills
Math Drill

Addition • Subtraction • Multiplication • Division • Fractions • Decimals

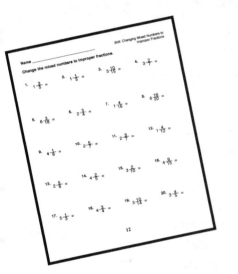

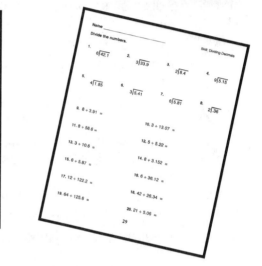

Basic math skills activities necessary for developing the skills students need to succeed!

Written by: Kelley Wingate Levy & Elizabeth E. Hanson

Look for all of Teacher's Friend's Basic Skills Books at your local educational retailer!

Table of Contents

teacher's friend publications

ISBN-0439-50189-9

Add the numbers.

1. 54
  + 79

2. 68
  + 45

3. 29
  + 37

4. 76
  + 55

5. 92
  + 88

6. 334
  + 608

7. 952
  + 431

8. 416
  + 653

9. 747
  + 513

10. 806
  + 391

11. 4,392
  + 646

12. 2,772
  + 533

13. 6,421
  + 763

14. 4,209
  + 443

15. 5,107
  + 894

16. 10,572
  + 6,104

17. 24,612
  + 3,407

18. 31,512
  + 4,271

19. 48,629
  + 5,310

20. 52,635
  + 50,128

21. 13,587
  + 25,145

22. 98,230
  + 12,454

23. 32,159
  + 74,581

Add the numbers.

1. 518
    463
    + 241

2. 325
    186
    + 239

3. 561
    254
    + 316

4. 432
    563
    + 316

5. 265
    617
    + 321

6. 89
    354
    + 1,642

7. 62
    295
    + 3,422

8. 38
    684
    + 5,219

9. 14
    423
    + 4,861

10. 54
    631
    + 3,824

11. 31,562
    2,725
    +   498

12. 17,431
    4,386
    +   545

13. 63,107
    5,428
    +   951

14. 28,236
    3,961
    +   492

15. 9,422
    536
    21
    +   11

16. 12,502
    604
    99
    +   21

17. 25,421
    1,528
    84
    +   50

18. 18,635
    4,029
    72
    +   10

4

Subtract the numbers.

1.   38
   - 24

2.   66
   - 52

3.   47
   - 17

4.   89
   - 62

5.   77
   - 64

6.   54
   - 35

7.   25
   - 16

8.   96
   - 45

9.   67
   - 55

10.   87
   - 62

11.   51
   - 45

12.   63
   - 48

13.   72
   - 59

14.   64
   - 58

15.   87
   - 78

16.   137
  - 108

17.   572
  - 269

18.   742
  - 398

19.   337
  - 294

20.   425
  - 394

21.   894
  - 409

22.   258
  - 176

23.   683
  - 558

24.   159
  - 123

25.   632
  - 541

Name _____

Subtract the numbers.

1. 9,864
    - 876

2. 5,502
    - 672

3. 8,217
    - 339

4. 3,201
    - 554

5. 4,791
    - 2,207

6. 3,792
    - 2,573

7. 7,784
    - 5,625

8. 7,987
    - 1,889

9. 6,895
    - 3,994

10. 9,452
     - 4,498

11. 5,542
     - 3,783

12. 3,787
     - 2,907

13. 5,623
     - 3,101

14. 8,745
     - 5,214

15. 3,511
     - 2,561

16. 37,423
     - 21,507

17. 67,898
     - 47,868

18. 84,302
     - 39,447

19. 56,402
     - 42,765

20. 12,453
     - 10,692

21. 45,987
     - 39,522

22. 71,902
     - 55,669

23. 34,522
     - 25,648

Name _____

Multiply the numbers.

1. $\begin{array}{r} 42 \\ \times\ 25 \\ \hline \end{array}$

2. $\begin{array}{r} 84 \\ \times\ 31 \\ \hline \end{array}$

3. $\begin{array}{r} 63 \\ \times\ 66 \\ \hline \end{array}$

4. $\begin{array}{r} 40 \\ \times\ 18 \\ \hline \end{array}$

5. $\begin{array}{r} 56 \\ \times\ 11 \\ \hline \end{array}$

6. $\begin{array}{r} 39 \\ \times\ 44 \\ \hline \end{array}$

7. $\begin{array}{r} 26 \\ \times\ 44 \\ \hline \end{array}$

8. $\begin{array}{r} 70 \\ \times\ 18 \\ \hline \end{array}$

9. $\begin{array}{r} 41 \\ \times\ 27 \\ \hline \end{array}$

10. $\begin{array}{r} 95 \\ \times\ 12 \\ \hline \end{array}$

11. $\begin{array}{r} 524 \\ \times\ 61 \\ \hline \end{array}$

12. $\begin{array}{r} 348 \\ \times\ 22 \\ \hline \end{array}$

13. $\begin{array}{r} 408 \\ \times\ 67 \\ \hline \end{array}$

14. $\begin{array}{r} 491 \\ \times\ 88 \\ \hline \end{array}$

15. $\begin{array}{r} 297 \\ \times\ 52 \\ \hline \end{array}$

16. $\begin{array}{r} 1{,}723 \\ \times\ 622 \\ \hline \end{array}$

17. $\begin{array}{r} 3{,}497 \\ \times\ 403 \\ \hline \end{array}$

18. $\begin{array}{r} 2{,}392 \\ \times\ 219 \\ \hline \end{array}$

19. $\begin{array}{r} 6{,}540 \\ \times\ 362 \\ \hline \end{array}$

20. $\begin{array}{r} 4{,}915 \\ \times\ 801 \\ \hline \end{array}$

21. $\begin{array}{r} 1{,}210 \\ \times\ 215 \\ \hline \end{array}$

22. $\begin{array}{r} 3{,}258 \\ \times\ 102 \\ \hline \end{array}$

23. $\begin{array}{r} 4{,}875 \\ \times\ 325 \\ \hline \end{array}$

24. $\begin{array}{r} 6{,}521 \\ \times\ 144 \\ \hline \end{array}$

25. $\begin{array}{r} 1{,}744 \\ \times\ 215 \\ \hline \end{array}$

Math Drill

Name _____

Multiply the numbers.

1.   105
   x 73

2.   219
   x 62

3.   453
   x 27

4.   138
   x 64

5.   223
   x 85

6.   6,502
   x 294

7.   3,016
   x 470

8.   2,123
   x 518

9.   1,806
   x 320

10.   4,519
   x 302

11.   2,404
   x 624

12.   5,203
   x 342

13.   1,412
   x 2,904

14.   4,302
   x 6,153

15.   2,962
   x 8,401

16.   5,620
   x 7,115

17.   8,490
   x 3,026

Name _____

Skill: Finding the Greatest Common Factor

List all of the factors of each pair of numbers, then give the greatest common factor (GCF).

	pair of numbers	factors	GCF
1.	6 and 10	6 = 10 =	
2.	12 and 10	12 = 10 =	
3.	20 and 30	20 = 30 =	
4.	8 and 40	8 = 40 =	
5.	18 and 8	18 = 8 =	
6.	48 and 36	48 = 36 =	
7.	40 and 60	40 = 60 =	
8.	8 and 27	8 = 27 =	
9.	24 and 56	24 = 56 =	
10.	36 and 54	36 = 54 =	

Teacher's Friend Publications ©   **9**   **TF-1334 Sixth Grade Basic Skills**
                                                                                                       Math Drill

Name _____

Write the first eight multiples of each number, then write the least common multiple (LCM).

	pair of numbers	multiples		LCM
1.	4 and 6	4 =	6 =	
2.	10 and 12	10 =	12 =	
3.	5 and 8	5 =	8 =	
4.	10 and 15	10 =	15 =	
5.	4 and 8	4 =	8 =	
6.	6 and 9	6 =	9 =	
7.	4 and 10	4 =	10 =	
8.	7 and 35	7 =	35 =	
9.	3 and 4	3 =	4 =	
10.	7 and 4	7 =	4 =	

Write each fraction in lowest terms.

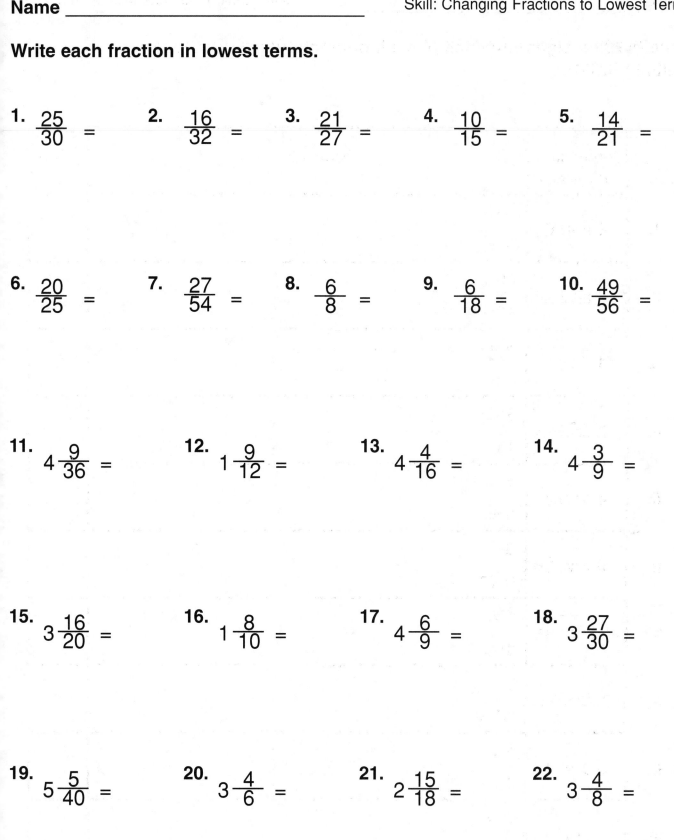

1. $\dfrac{25}{30}$ =

2. $\dfrac{16}{32}$ =

3. $\dfrac{21}{27}$ =

4. $\dfrac{10}{15}$ =

5. $\dfrac{14}{21}$ =

6. $\dfrac{20}{25}$ =

7. $\dfrac{27}{54}$ =

8. $\dfrac{6}{8}$ =

9. $\dfrac{6}{18}$ =

10. $\dfrac{49}{56}$ =

11. $4\dfrac{9}{36}$ =

12. $1\dfrac{9}{12}$ =

13. $4\dfrac{4}{16}$ =

14. $4\dfrac{3}{9}$ =

15. $3\dfrac{16}{20}$ =

16. $1\dfrac{8}{10}$ =

17. $4\dfrac{6}{9}$ =

18. $3\dfrac{27}{30}$ =

19. $5\dfrac{5}{40}$ =

20. $3\dfrac{4}{6}$ =

21. $2\dfrac{15}{18}$ =

22. $3\dfrac{4}{8}$ =

Change the mixed numbers to improper fractions.

1. $1\frac{3}{5} =$

2. $1\frac{1}{5} =$

3. $5\frac{10}{15} =$

4. $3\frac{2}{7} =$

5. $6\frac{3}{18} =$

6. $2\frac{3}{4} =$

7. $1\frac{4}{16} =$

8. $6\frac{16}{20} =$

9. $4\frac{1}{6} =$

10. $2\frac{5}{7} =$

11. $2\frac{3}{7} =$

12. $1\frac{4}{12} =$

13. $2\frac{5}{6} =$

14. $4\frac{2}{5} =$

15. $3\frac{2}{10} =$

16. $4\frac{9}{15} =$

17. $5\frac{1}{3} =$

18. $4\frac{3}{4} =$

19. $3\frac{10}{14} =$

20. $3\frac{4}{5} =$

Change each improper fraction to a mixed number.

1. $\dfrac{34}{9}$ =

2. $\dfrac{55}{7}$ =

3. $\dfrac{51}{4}$ =

4. $\dfrac{22}{3}$ =

5. $\dfrac{65}{8}$ =

6. $\dfrac{85}{6}$ =

7. $\dfrac{47}{5}$ =

8. $\dfrac{67}{11}$ =

9. $\dfrac{25}{2}$ =

10. $\dfrac{211}{10}$ =

11. $\dfrac{180}{13}$ =

12. $\dfrac{38}{9}$ =

13. $\dfrac{77}{9}$ =

14. $\dfrac{83}{10}$ =

15. $\dfrac{44}{15}$ =

16. $\dfrac{143}{20}$ =

17. $\dfrac{73}{11}$ =

18. $\dfrac{79}{9}$ =

19. $\dfrac{47}{5}$ =

20. $\dfrac{75}{6}$ =

Name _____

Add the fractions and reduce your answer to lowest terms.

1. $\dfrac{1}{5} + \dfrac{3}{5} =$

2. $\dfrac{1}{4} + \dfrac{2}{4} =$

3. $\dfrac{2}{6} + \dfrac{3}{6} =$

4. $\dfrac{3}{9} + \dfrac{4}{9} =$

5. $\dfrac{4}{7} + \dfrac{5}{7} =$

6. $\dfrac{1}{3} + \dfrac{1}{3} =$

7. $\dfrac{2}{10} + \dfrac{6}{10} =$

8. $\dfrac{1}{5} + \dfrac{4}{5} =$

9. $\dfrac{5}{15} + \dfrac{7}{15} =$

10. $\dfrac{1}{6} + \dfrac{5}{6} =$

11. $\dfrac{3}{8} + \dfrac{7}{8} =$

12. $\dfrac{6}{12} + \dfrac{4}{12} =$

13. $\dfrac{5}{10} + \dfrac{7}{10} =$

14. $\dfrac{6}{7} + \dfrac{4}{7} =$

15. $\dfrac{9}{18} + \dfrac{7}{18} =$

16. $\dfrac{2}{4} + \dfrac{4}{4} =$

17. $\dfrac{4}{11} + \dfrac{9}{11} =$

18. $\dfrac{5}{6} + \dfrac{3}{6} =$

Add the fractions and reduce your answer to lowest terms.

1. $\dfrac{1}{5} + \dfrac{1}{3} =$

2. $\dfrac{2}{5} + \dfrac{1}{2} =$

3. $\dfrac{7}{8} + \dfrac{1}{16} =$

4. $\dfrac{4}{5} + \dfrac{1}{10} =$

5. $\dfrac{2}{5} + \dfrac{3}{4} =$

6. $\dfrac{1}{4} + \dfrac{3}{8} =$

7. $\dfrac{5}{6} + \dfrac{7}{9} =$

8. $\dfrac{5}{14} + \dfrac{1}{2} =$

9. $\dfrac{1}{4} + \dfrac{1}{5} =$

10. $\dfrac{1}{6} + \dfrac{2}{9} =$

11. $\dfrac{2}{3} + \dfrac{1}{4} =$

12. $\dfrac{1}{3} + \dfrac{1}{9} =$

13. $\dfrac{4}{5} + \dfrac{7}{15} =$

14. $\dfrac{7}{12} + \dfrac{5}{36} =$

15. $\dfrac{2}{9} + \dfrac{4}{5} =$

16. $\dfrac{1}{6} + \dfrac{3}{3} =$

17. $\dfrac{3}{5} + \dfrac{9}{20} =$

18. $\dfrac{1}{2} + \dfrac{5}{7} =$

Name _____

Add the mixed numbers and reduce your answer to lowest terms.

1. $2\frac{1}{3} + 3\frac{1}{3} =$

2. $5\frac{4}{5} + 2\frac{3}{7} =$

3. $4\frac{2}{3} + 3\frac{1}{4} =$

4. $1\frac{3}{8} + 1\frac{2}{4} =$

5. $3\frac{1}{2} + 5\frac{2}{6} =$

6. $1\frac{3}{4} + 5\frac{1}{2} =$

7. $6\frac{1}{5} + 3\frac{1}{2} =$

8. $2\frac{1}{8} + 4\frac{1}{4} =$

9. $9\frac{2}{3} + 6\frac{1}{2} =$

10. $4\frac{2}{5} + 1\frac{3}{4} =$

11. $4\frac{2}{3} + 1\frac{2}{5} =$

12. $8\frac{2}{3} + 6\frac{4}{5} =$

Name _____

Subtract the fractions and reduce your answer to lowest terms.

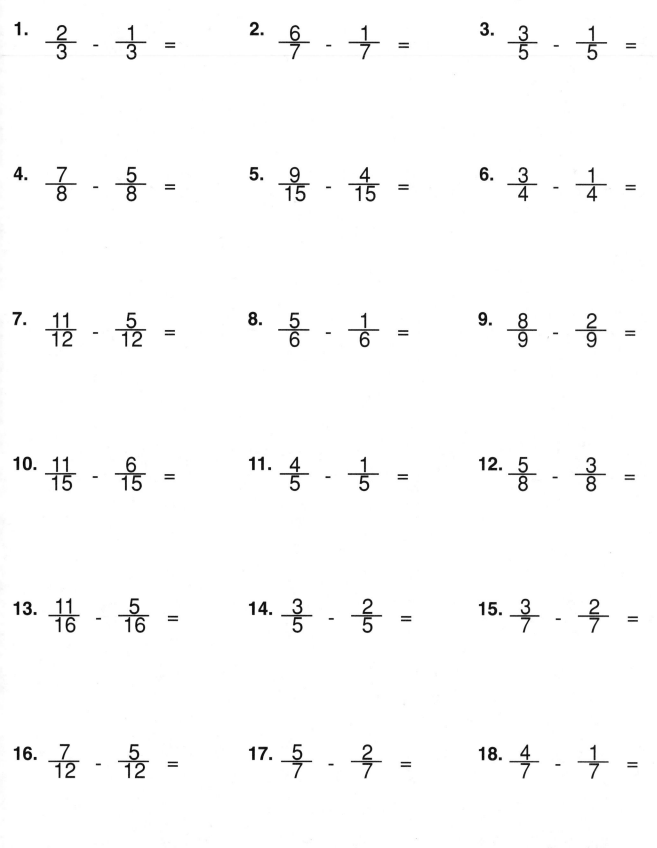

1. $\dfrac{2}{3} - \dfrac{1}{3} =$

2. $\dfrac{6}{7} - \dfrac{1}{7} =$

3. $\dfrac{3}{5} - \dfrac{1}{5} =$

4. $\dfrac{7}{8} - \dfrac{5}{8} =$

5. $\dfrac{9}{15} - \dfrac{4}{15} =$

6. $\dfrac{3}{4} - \dfrac{1}{4} =$

7. $\dfrac{11}{12} - \dfrac{5}{12} =$

8. $\dfrac{5}{6} - \dfrac{1}{6} =$

9. $\dfrac{8}{9} - \dfrac{2}{9} =$

10. $\dfrac{11}{15} - \dfrac{6}{15} =$

11. $\dfrac{4}{5} - \dfrac{1}{5} =$

12. $\dfrac{5}{8} - \dfrac{3}{8} =$

13. $\dfrac{11}{16} - \dfrac{5}{16} =$

14. $\dfrac{3}{5} - \dfrac{2}{5} =$

15. $\dfrac{3}{7} - \dfrac{2}{7} =$

16. $\dfrac{7}{12} - \dfrac{5}{12} =$

17. $\dfrac{5}{7} - \dfrac{2}{7} =$

18. $\dfrac{4}{7} - \dfrac{1}{7} =$

Subtract the fractions and reduce your answer to lowest terms.

1. $\dfrac{4}{5} - \dfrac{1}{3} =$

2. $\dfrac{9}{10} - \dfrac{1}{3} =$

3. $\dfrac{7}{8} - \dfrac{5}{12} =$

4. $\dfrac{1}{6} - \dfrac{1}{9} =$

5. $\dfrac{1}{5} - \dfrac{1}{8} =$

6. $\dfrac{5}{6} - \dfrac{2}{7} =$

7. $\dfrac{6}{7} - \dfrac{9}{14} =$

8. $\dfrac{11}{12} - \dfrac{1}{3} =$

9. $\dfrac{7}{8} - \dfrac{1}{4} =$

10. $\dfrac{3}{4} - \dfrac{2}{9} =$

11. $\dfrac{1}{2} - \dfrac{3}{11} =$

12. $\dfrac{5}{8} - \dfrac{1}{2} =$

13. $\dfrac{7}{10} - \dfrac{2}{5} =$

14. $\dfrac{7}{9} - \dfrac{1}{3} =$

15. $\dfrac{7}{8} - \dfrac{1}{2} =$

16. $\dfrac{3}{4} - \dfrac{2}{3} =$

17. $\dfrac{4}{5} - \dfrac{1}{3} =$

18. $\dfrac{7}{8} - \dfrac{2}{3} =$

Name _____

Find the lowest common demonitor, subtract the mixed numbers and reduce your answer to lowest terms.

1. $5\dfrac{1}{3} - 2\dfrac{3}{8} =$

2. $9\dfrac{3}{4} - 1\dfrac{1}{5} =$

3. $7\dfrac{1}{5} - 6\dfrac{3}{15} =$

4. $5\dfrac{4}{5} - 5\dfrac{5}{7} =$

5. $10\dfrac{1}{9} - 6\dfrac{2}{3} =$

6. $2\dfrac{3}{7} - 1\dfrac{7}{8} =$

7. $8\dfrac{5}{8} - 3\dfrac{4}{5} =$

8. $3\dfrac{4}{9} - 2\dfrac{2}{3} =$

9. $6\dfrac{3}{5} - 3\dfrac{7}{10} =$

10. $9\dfrac{7}{9} - 4\dfrac{1}{7} =$

11. $4\dfrac{1}{4} - 2\dfrac{5}{8} =$

12. $6\dfrac{5}{7} - 4\dfrac{7}{12} =$

Name _____

Multiply the fractions and reduce your answer to lowest terms.

1. $\dfrac{1}{3} \times \dfrac{12}{15} =$

2. $\dfrac{15}{24} \times \dfrac{8}{9} =$

3. $\dfrac{3}{4} \times \dfrac{2}{9} =$

4. $\dfrac{7}{36} \times \dfrac{9}{14} =$

5. $\dfrac{10}{15} \times \dfrac{2}{4} =$

6. $\dfrac{3}{5} \times \dfrac{5}{7} =$

7. $\dfrac{9}{10} \times \dfrac{2}{3} =$

8. $\dfrac{7}{9} \times \dfrac{15}{21} =$

9. $\dfrac{3}{20} \times \dfrac{5}{7} =$

10. $\dfrac{3}{4} \times \dfrac{7}{12} =$

11. $\dfrac{5}{6} \times \dfrac{3}{4} =$

12. $\dfrac{1}{5} \times \dfrac{5}{9} =$

13. $\dfrac{3}{14} \times \dfrac{7}{16} =$

14. $\dfrac{12}{25} \times \dfrac{15}{24} =$

15. $\dfrac{3}{8} \times \dfrac{24}{25} =$

16. $\dfrac{5}{16} \times \dfrac{4}{5} =$

17. $\dfrac{5}{14} \times \dfrac{7}{10} =$

18. $\dfrac{5}{8} \times \dfrac{9}{20} =$

Multiply the fractions and reduce your answer to lowest terms.

1. $5 \times \dfrac{2}{3} =$

2. $7 \times \dfrac{1}{5} =$

3. $2 \times \dfrac{5}{8} =$

4. $3 \times \dfrac{1}{7} =$

5. $5 \times \dfrac{1}{8} =$

6. $8 \times \dfrac{5}{7} =$

7. $9 \times \dfrac{1}{3} =$

8. $6 \times \dfrac{5}{6} =$

9. $10 \times \dfrac{2}{7} =$

10. $1 \times \dfrac{1}{2} =$

11. $4 \times \dfrac{3}{5} =$

12. $3 \times \dfrac{7}{9} =$

13. $2 \times \dfrac{2}{9} =$

14. $4 \times \dfrac{2}{5} =$

15. $6 \times \dfrac{7}{10} =$

16. $9 \times \dfrac{3}{8} =$

17. $4 \times \dfrac{7}{12} =$

18. $8 \times \dfrac{1}{6} =$

Name _____

Divide the fractions and reduce your answer to lowest terms.

1. $\dfrac{1}{3} \div \dfrac{1}{6} =$

2. $\dfrac{5}{6} \div \dfrac{2}{3} =$

3. $\dfrac{7}{12} \div \dfrac{1}{4} =$

4. $\dfrac{1}{9} \div \dfrac{2}{3} =$

5. $\dfrac{10}{11} \div \dfrac{2}{5} =$

6. $\dfrac{7}{8} \div \dfrac{5}{24} =$

7. $\dfrac{4}{5} \div \dfrac{7}{10} =$

8. $\dfrac{11}{12} \div \dfrac{3}{4} =$

9. $\dfrac{9}{20} \div \dfrac{3}{5} =$

10. $\dfrac{9}{14} \div \dfrac{3}{7} =$

11. $\dfrac{17}{20} \div \dfrac{5}{20} =$

12. $\dfrac{5}{12} \div \dfrac{15}{24} =$

13. $\dfrac{4}{5} \div \dfrac{1}{10} =$

14. $\dfrac{1}{6} \div \dfrac{7}{24} =$

15. $\dfrac{15}{16} \div \dfrac{3}{4} =$

16. $\dfrac{11}{18} \div \dfrac{2}{9} =$

17. $\dfrac{14}{27} \div \dfrac{7}{9} =$

18. $\dfrac{13}{30} \div \dfrac{1}{15} =$

Divide the fractions and whole numbers and reduce your answer to lowest terms.

1. $\dfrac{4}{5} \div 2 =$

2. $9 \div \dfrac{9}{10} =$

3. $\dfrac{4}{7} \div 8 =$

4. $3 \div \dfrac{6}{7} =$

5. $15 \div \dfrac{2}{3} =$

6. $7 \div \dfrac{21}{22} =$

7. $\dfrac{3}{4} \div 11 =$

8. $12 \div \dfrac{3}{11} =$

9. $18 \div \dfrac{3}{5} =$

10. $14 \div \dfrac{2}{5} =$

11. $1 \div \dfrac{5}{8} =$

12. $\dfrac{1}{8} \div 4 =$

13. $5 \div \dfrac{10}{13} =$

14. $9 \div \dfrac{6}{15} =$

15. $\dfrac{3}{8} \div 21 =$

16. $16 \div \dfrac{4}{9} =$

17. $\dfrac{2}{7} \div 10 =$

18. $20 \div \dfrac{5}{9} =$

Divide the fractions and mixed numbers and reduce your answer to lowest terms.

1.
$$4\frac{2}{7} \div \frac{1}{4} =$$

2.
$$1\frac{3}{7} \div \frac{1}{3} =$$

3.
$$4\frac{6}{7} \div \frac{1}{3} =$$

4.
$$\frac{2}{3} \div 1\frac{7}{9} =$$

5.
$$\frac{1}{3} \div 1\frac{5}{6} =$$

6.
$$3\frac{9}{10} \div \frac{1}{6} =$$

7.
$$3\frac{7}{8} \div \frac{2}{3} =$$

8.
$$\frac{1}{3} \div 5\frac{5}{9} =$$

9.
$$8\frac{1}{4} \div \frac{1}{6} =$$

10.
$$\frac{3}{8} \div 5\frac{5}{6} =$$

11.
$$\frac{3}{4} \div 5\frac{1}{7} =$$

12.
$$3\frac{6}{7} \div \frac{1}{5} =$$

Name _____

Fill in the missing part of each pair of fractions to make them equivalent.

1. $\dfrac{3}{4} = \dfrac{}{16}$

2. $\dfrac{2}{3} = \dfrac{6}{}$

3. $\dfrac{7}{15} = \dfrac{}{45}$

4. $\dfrac{4}{5} = \dfrac{20}{}$

5. $\dfrac{3}{8} = \dfrac{}{32}$

6. $\dfrac{5}{9} = \dfrac{15}{}$

7. $\dfrac{7}{8} = \dfrac{}{24}$

8. $\dfrac{7}{12} = \dfrac{14}{}$

In each row, circle the fractions that are equivalent to the first fraction.

9. $\dfrac{1}{3}$ $\dfrac{3}{9}$ $\dfrac{9}{10}$ $\dfrac{2}{6}$ $\dfrac{5}{15}$ $\dfrac{6}{17}$ $\dfrac{4}{12}$

10. $\dfrac{2}{5}$ $\dfrac{10}{25}$ $\dfrac{8}{22}$ $\dfrac{16}{45}$ $\dfrac{4}{10}$ $\dfrac{14}{35}$ $\dfrac{12}{30}$

11. $\dfrac{3}{7}$ $\dfrac{24}{58}$ $\dfrac{9}{21}$ $\dfrac{30}{60}$ $\dfrac{12}{28}$ $\dfrac{15}{35}$ $\dfrac{24}{56}$

12. $\dfrac{4}{5}$ $\dfrac{12}{25}$ $\dfrac{20}{30}$ $\dfrac{16}{20}$ $\dfrac{28}{35}$ $\dfrac{12}{15}$ $\dfrac{8}{10}$

13. $\dfrac{7}{8}$ $\dfrac{14}{16}$ $\dfrac{35}{45}$ $\dfrac{28}{32}$ $\dfrac{21}{24}$ $\dfrac{42}{48}$ $\dfrac{49}{72}$

14. $\dfrac{1}{6}$ $\dfrac{5}{30}$ $\dfrac{2}{12}$ $\dfrac{3}{36}$ $\dfrac{3}{18}$ $\dfrac{8}{36}$ $\dfrac{10}{60}$

15. $\dfrac{5}{6}$ $\dfrac{25}{30}$ $\dfrac{15}{18}$ $\dfrac{10}{18}$ $\dfrac{20}{24}$ $\dfrac{30}{25}$ $\dfrac{45}{54}$

Add the numbers.

1. $\begin{array}{r} 63.807 \\ +\ 1.054 \\ \hline \end{array}$

2. $\begin{array}{r} 2.368 \\ +\ .257 \\ \hline \end{array}$

3. $\begin{array}{r} 46.315 \\ +\ 9.887 \\ \hline \end{array}$

4. $\begin{array}{r} 123.021 \\ +\ 6.009 \\ \hline \end{array}$

5. $\begin{array}{r} 42.046 \\ +\ .3201 \\ \hline \end{array}$

6. $\begin{array}{r} 162.09 \\ +\ 1.066 \\ \hline \end{array}$

7. $\begin{array}{r} 62.2 \\ +\ .0083 \\ \hline \end{array}$

8. $\begin{array}{r} 27.437 \\ +\ 1.00215 \\ \hline \end{array}$

9. 31.426 + 27.2 =

10. .045 + 62.7 =

11. 3,214.6 + 2.504 =

12. 10.05 + 312.625 =

13. 14 + .005 =

14. .5 + 12.761 =

15. 99.9 + 1.99 =

16. 5.73 + 1.0024 =

17. 3.5 + 4.5 =

18. .059 + 22.6 =

19. 86.982 + .404 =

20. 5.711 + 142.08 =

Subtract the numbers.

1.
$$\begin{array}{r} 30.62 \\ -\ 15.01 \\ \hline \end{array}$$

2.
$$\begin{array}{r} 721.83 \\ -\ \ \ .42 \\ \hline \end{array}$$

3.
$$\begin{array}{r} 39.628 \\ -\ 11.64 \\ \hline \end{array}$$

4.
$$\begin{array}{r} 26.02 \\ -\ 3.14 \\ \hline \end{array}$$

5.
$$\begin{array}{r} 17.602 \\ -\ 4.98 \\ \hline \end{array}$$

6.
$$\begin{array}{r} 37.509 \\ -\ 24.7 \\ \hline \end{array}$$

7.
$$\begin{array}{r} 225.99 \\ -\ \ .027 \\ \hline \end{array}$$

8.
$$\begin{array}{r} 241.62 \\ -\ 80.4 \\ \hline \end{array}$$

9. $42.6 - 24.062 =$

10. $67.502 - 25.4 =$

11. $396.09 - 71.225 =$

12. $42.65 - 27.109 =$

13. $584.6 - .0047 =$

14. $17.401 - 3.52 =$

15. $471.55 - 32.0627 =$

16. $12.94 - 9.062 =$

17. $47.02 - 13.088 =$

18. $88.65 - 17.92 =$

19. $4.003 - 3.4 =$

20. $22.6 - 9.332 =$

Multiply the numbers.

1.
```
    42.7
x  6.809
```

2.
```
    13.6
x    22.7
```

3.
```
   40.301
x    6.07
```

4.
```
   99.12
x    8.6
```

5.
```
   4.23
x    6.5
```

6.
```
     1.5
x  6.07
```

7.
```
   13.8
x   5.6
```

8.
```
    .012
x   .75
```

9. 6.49 x 3.21 =

10. .481 x 39.5 =

11. 87.4 x .51 =

12. 6.35 x 2.9 =

13. 27.6 x .17 =

14. 45.1 x .35 =

15. 4.13 x .35 =

16. 6.21 x 2.7 =

17. 28.2 x .38 =

18. 1.2 x 44 =

19. 2.57 x 53.5 =

20. 5.12 x 2.83 =

Name _____

Divide the numbers.

1.

$6\overline{)42.1}$

2.

$3\overline{)33.9}$

3.

$2\overline{)8.4}$

4.

$9\overline{)5.15}$

5.

$4\overline{)1.85}$

6.

$3\overline{)5.41}$

7.

$6\overline{)5.81}$

8.

$2\overline{).36}$

9. $8 \div 3.91 =$

10. $3 \div 13.07 =$

11. $8 \div 58.6 =$

12. $5 \div 5.22 =$

13. $3 \div 10.6 =$

14. $8 \div 3.152 =$

15. $6 \div 5.87 =$

16. $6 \div 36.12 =$

17. $12 \div 122.2 =$

18. $42 \div 26.34 =$

19. $64 \div 125.6 =$

20. $21 \div 5.06 =$

Change the fractions or mixed numbers to decimals.

1. $\dfrac{7}{20}$ =

2. $\dfrac{3}{4}$ =

3. $\dfrac{1}{2}$ =

4. $\dfrac{9}{10}$ =

5. $\dfrac{3}{8}$ =

6. $2\dfrac{5}{8}$ =

7. $4\dfrac{3}{10}$ =

8. $\dfrac{7}{10}$ =

9. $\dfrac{9}{20}$ =

10. $3\dfrac{2}{5}$ =

11. $6\dfrac{4}{25}$ =

12. $\dfrac{3}{40}$ =

13. $\dfrac{7}{50}$ =

14. $\dfrac{19}{20}$ =

15. $\dfrac{1}{8}$ =

16. $2\dfrac{1}{5}$ =

17. $\dfrac{3}{5}$ =

18. $6\dfrac{1}{4}$ =

19. $\dfrac{11}{20}$ =

20. $\dfrac{4}{5}$ =

Name _____

Change each decimal to a fraction or mixed number.

1. .16 =

2. 2.07 =

3. 2.7 =

4. .87 =

5. 6.5 =

6. 5.9 =

7. 3.75 =

8. 4.125 =

9. 1.4 =

10. .6 =

11. 4.2 =

12. 6.8 =

13. .375 =

14. .35 =

15. .62 =

16. .256 =

17. 2.02 =

18. .05 =

19. .18 =

20. 3.03 =

Name _____

Change each percentage to a fraction.

1. 1% =   **2.** 224% =   **3.** 14% =   **4.** 30% =

5. 18% =   **6.** 22% =   **7.** 85% =   **8.** 2% =

9. 115% =   **10.** 95% =   **11.** 20% =   **12.** 40% =

13. 100% =   **14.** 156% =   **15.** 12% =   **16.** 4% =

17. 11% =   **18.** 145% =   **19.** 42% =   **20.** 78% =

Name _____

Change each fraction to a percentage.

1. $\dfrac{3}{4}$ =

2. $\dfrac{1}{4}$ =

3. $\dfrac{8}{10}$ =

4. $\dfrac{3}{100}$ =

5. $1\dfrac{1}{2}$ =

6. $\dfrac{4}{25}$ =

7. $\dfrac{6}{20}$ =

8. $\dfrac{3}{25}$ =

9. $\dfrac{9}{10}$ =

10. $1\dfrac{1}{4}$ =

11. $\dfrac{55}{100}$ =

12. $\dfrac{2}{25}$ =

13. $\dfrac{1}{2}$ =

14. $\dfrac{7}{10}$ =

15. $\dfrac{6}{25}$ =

16. $\dfrac{1}{20}$ =

17. $\dfrac{1}{10}$ =

18. $\dfrac{6}{10}$ =

19. $1\dfrac{3}{4}$ =

20. $\dfrac{9}{20}$ =

Change each percentage to a decimal.

1. 18% =   2. 25% =   3. 76% =   4. 16% =

5. 199% =   6. 33% =   7. 43% =   8. 52% =

9. 408% =   10. 89% =   11. 63% =   12. 182% =

13. 30% =   14. 6% =   15. 12% =   16. 7% =

17. 240% =   18. 95% =   19. 99% =   20. 4% =

Complete the chart by filling in the empty spaces, making each row equivalent.

	Fraction	Decimal	Percentage
1.			25%
2.		.02	
3.	$\frac{2}{8}$		
4.			70%
5.		.45	
6.	$\frac{1}{10}$		
7.			42%
8.		.2	
9.	$\frac{4}{5}$		
10.			32%

Name _____

The sixth grade class had a bake sale. The graph below shows the quantity of each item sold.

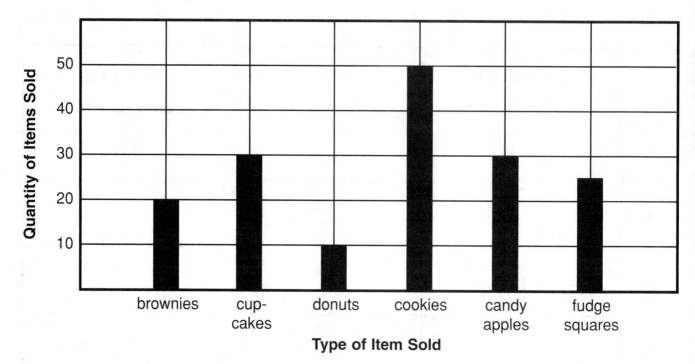

Answer the questions below using the bar graph.

1. Which item did the class sell the most of? _____

2. What two items did the class sell the same amount of?

_____

3. About how many fudge squares were sold? _____

4. How many brownies, donuts, and cookies were sold all together? _____

5. Which item did the class sell the least of? _____

The line graph below shows how many points the Center City Panthers scored during each of their football games last season.

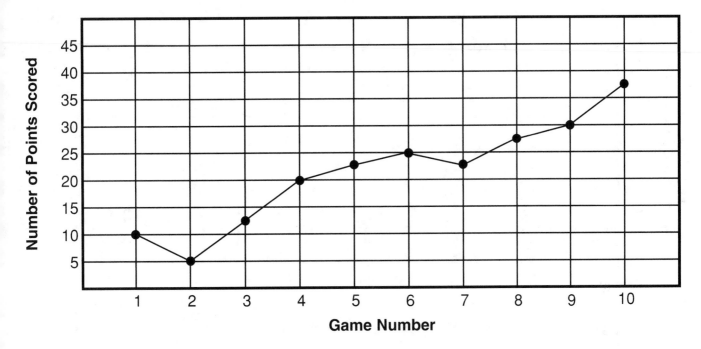

Answer the questions below using the line graph.

1. In which game did the Panthers score the most points? _____

2. In which games did the Panthers score 12, 20, and 28 points?

_____

3. How many points were scored in all in games number 2, 4, 6, and 9?_____

4. In which game did the Panthers score the least number of points? _____

5. Did the Panthers improve in their scoring by the end of the year? _____

Name _____

Multiply the numbers.

1. 358	**2.** 548	**3.** 2,144	**4.** 3,224	**5.** 8,114
x 56	x 256	x 247	x 612	x 5,264

Write each fraction in lowest terms.

6. $\dfrac{16}{24}$ =   **7.** $\dfrac{9}{27}$ =   **8.** $\dfrac{56}{64}$ =   **9.** $\dfrac{12}{16}$ =   **10.** $\dfrac{30}{45}$ =

Rewrite each improper fraction as a mixed number.

11. $\dfrac{35}{6}$ =   **12.** $\dfrac{58}{12}$ =   **13.** $\dfrac{132}{54}$ =   **14.** $\dfrac{95}{9}$ =

Rewrite each mixed number as an improper fraction.

15. $3\dfrac{9}{10}$ =   **16.** $2\dfrac{7}{8}$ =   **17.** $6\dfrac{2}{3}$ =   **18.** $8\dfrac{5}{6}$ =

Add the fractions.

19. $\dfrac{2}{5} + \dfrac{3}{8}$ =   **20.** $\dfrac{1}{3} + \dfrac{2}{7}$ =   **21.** $\dfrac{23}{27} + \dfrac{8}{9}$ =

Add the mixed numbers.

22. $4\frac{2}{7} + 3\frac{11}{14} =$

23. $3\frac{3}{5} + 4\frac{1}{8} =$

Subtract the fractions.

24. $\frac{5}{6} - \frac{1}{3} =$

25. $\frac{7}{9} - \frac{3}{8} =$

26. $\frac{9}{10} - \frac{3}{5} =$

Subtract the mixed numbers.

27. $5\frac{2}{3} - 4\frac{2}{9} =$

28. $8\frac{5}{6} - 5\frac{3}{5} =$

Multiply the fractions.

29. $\frac{2}{3} \times \frac{1}{8} =$

30. $\frac{1}{5} \times \frac{10}{13} =$

31. $\frac{4}{7} \times \frac{14}{15} =$

Divide the fractions.

32. $\frac{10}{11} \div \frac{15}{22} =$

33. $\frac{3}{4} \div \frac{15}{16} =$

34. $\frac{9}{10} \div \frac{2}{3} =$

Name _____

Fill in the missing part of each pair of fractions to make them equivalent.

35. $\dfrac{5}{6} = \dfrac{25}{}$ **36.** $\dfrac{3}{8} = \dfrac{}{24}$ **37.** $\dfrac{8}{15} = \dfrac{}{45}$ **38.** $\dfrac{6}{7} = \dfrac{42}{}$

Add the decimals.

39. $6.002 + 12.5 =$

40. $31.426 + 25.8 =$

41. $15.263 + .12 =$

42. $105.2 + 2.199 =$

Subtract the decimals.

43. $4.35 - 2.005 =$

44. $28.54 - 1.052 =$

45. $9.891 - 1.2 =$

46. $62.451 - .118 =$

Multiply the decimals.

47. $6.2 \times 12.43 =$

48. $.25 \times 1.75 =$

49. $2.5 \times .175 =$

50. $1.008 \times 16.2 =$

Divide the decimals.

51. $3.12 \div 4.4 =$

52. $1.25 \div 2.5 =$

53. $.048 \div 8 =$

54. $16.4 \div .82 =$

Math Drill

Name _____

Change each fraction to a decimal.

55. $\dfrac{7}{20}$ =

56. $\dfrac{1}{8}$ =

57. $\dfrac{3}{21}$ =

58. $\dfrac{6}{50}$ =

Change each decimal to a fraction or mixed number.

59. .24 =

60. 3.67 =

61. 8.16 =

62. 9.55 =

Change each percentage to a decimal.

63. 65% =

64. 33% =

65. 152% =

66. 8% =

Change each fraction to a percentage.

67. $\dfrac{6}{10}$ =

68. $\dfrac{3}{8}$ =

69. $\dfrac{1}{5}$ =

70. $\dfrac{25}{100}$ =

Change each percentage to a fraction.

71. 10% =

72. 15% =

73. 52% =

74. 65% =

Answer Key

Page 5

Skill: Subtracting Two & Three digit Numbers

Name _____

Subtract the numbers.

#	Problem	Answer
1.	38 − 24	14
2.	66 − 52	14
3.	47 − 17	30
4.	89 − 62	27
5.	77 − 64	13
6.	54 − 35	19
7.	25 − 16	9
8.	96 − 45	51
9.	67 − 55	12
10.	87 − 62	25
11.	51 − 45	6
12.	63 − 48	15
13.	72 − 59	13
14.	64 − 58	6
15.	87 − 78	9
16.	137 − 108	29
17.	572 − 269	303
18.	742 − 398	344
19.	337 − 294	43
20.	425 − 394	31
21.	894 − 409	485
22.	258 − 176	82
23.	683 − 558	125
24.	159 − 123	36
25.	632 − 541	91

5

Page 8

Skill: Multiplying Two, Three and Four Digit Numbers

Name _____

Multiply the numbers.

#	Problem	Answer
1.	105 × 73	7,665
2.	219 × 62	13,578
3.	453 × 27	12,231
4.	138 × 64	8,832
5.	223 × 85	18,955
6.	6,502 × 294	1,911,588
7.	3,016 × 470	1,417,520
8.	2,123 × 518	1,099,714
9.	1,806 × 320	577,920
10.	4,519 × 302	1,364,738
11.	2,404 × 624	1,500,096
12.	5,203 × 342	1,779,426
13.	1,412 × 2,904	4,100,448
14.	4,302 × 6,153	26,470,206
15.	2,962 × 8,401	24,883,762
16.	5,620 × 7,115	39,986,300
17.	8,490 × 3,026	25,690,740

8

Page 4

Skill: Adding Two, Three, Four, and Five Digit Numbers

Name _____

Add the numbers.

#	Problem	Answer
1.	518 + 463 + 241	1,222
2.	325 + 186 + 239	750
3.	561 + 254 + 316	1,131
4.	432 + 563 + 316	1,311
5.	265 + 617 + 321	1,203
6.	89 + 354 + 1,642	2,085
7.	62 + 295 + 3,422	3,779
8.	38 + 684 + 5,219	5,941
9.	14 + 423 + 4,861	5,298
10.	54 + 631 + 3,824	4,509
11.	31,562 + 2,725 + 498	34,785
12.	17,431 + 4,386 + 545	22,362
13.	63,107 + 5,428 + 951	69,486
14.	28,236 + 3,961 + 492	32,689
15.	9,422 + 536 + 21 + 11	9,990
16.	12,502 + 604 + 99 + 21	13,226
17.	25,421 + 1,528 + 84 + 50	27,083
18.	18,635 + 4,029 + 72 + 10	22,746

4

Page 7

Skill: Multiplying Two, Three, Four Digit Numbers

Name _____

Multiply the numbers.

#	Problem	Answer
1.	42 × 25	1,050
2.	84 × 31	2,604
3.	63 × 66	4,158
4.	40 × 18	720
5.	56 × 11	616
6.	39 × 44	1,716
7.	26 × 44	1,144
8.	70 × 18	1,260
9.	41 × 27	1,107
10.	95 × 12	1,140
11.	524 × 61	31,964
12.	348 × 22	7,656
13.	408 × 67	27,336
14.	491 × 88	43,208
15.	297 × 52	15,444
16.	1,723 × 622	1,071,706
17.	3,497 × 403	1,409,291
18.	2,392 × 219	523,848
19.	6,540 × 362	2,367,480
20.	4,915 × 801	3,936,915
21.	1,210 × 215	260,150
22.	3,258 × 102	332,316
23.	4,875 × 325	1,584,375
24.	6,521 × 144	939,024
25.	1,744 × 215	374,960

7

Page 3

Skill: Adding Two, Three, Four and Five Digit Numbers

Name _____

Add the numbers.

#	Problem	Answer
1.	54 + 79	133
2.	68 + 45	113
3.	29 + 37	66
4.	76 + 55	131
5.	92 + 88	180
6.	334 + 608	942
7.	952 + 431	1,383
8.	416 + 653	1,069
9.	747 + 513	1,260
10.	806 + 391	1,197
11.	4,392 + 646	5,038
12.	2,772 + 533	3,305
13.	6,421 + 763	7,184
14.	4,209 + 443	4,652
15.	5,107 + 894	6,001
16.	10,572 + 6,104	16,676
17.	24,612 + 3,407	28,019
18.	31,512 + 4,271	35,783
19.	48,629 + 5,310	53,939
20.	52,635 + 50,128	102,763
21.	13,587 + 25,145	38,732
22.	98,230 + 12,454	110,684
23.	32,159 + 74,581	106,740

3

Page 6

Skill: Subtracting Three, Four and Five Digit Numbers

Name _____

Subtract the numbers.

#	Problem	Answer
1.	9,864 − 876	8,988
2.	5,502 − 672	4,830
3.	8,217 − 339	7,878
4.	3,201 − 554	2,647
5.	4,791 − 2,207	2,584
6.	3,792 − 2,573	1,219
7.	7,784 − 5,625	2,159
8.	7,987 − 1,889	6,098
9.	6,895 − 3,994	2,901
10.	9,452 − 4,498	4,954
11.	5,542 − 3,783	1,759
12.	3,787 − 2,907	880
13.	5,623 − 3,101	2,522
14.	8,745 − 5,214	3,531
15.	3,511 − 2,561	950
16.	37,423 − 21,507	15,916
17.	67,898 − 47,868	20,030
18.	84,302 − 39,447	44,855
19.	56,402 − 42,765	13,637
20.	12,453 − 10,692	1,761
21.	45,987 − 39,522	6,465
22.	71,902 − 55,669	16,233
23.	34,522 − 25,648	8,874

6

Answer Key

Page 11

Name _____   Skill: Changing Fractions to Lowest Terms

Write each fraction in lowest terms.

1. $\frac{25}{30} = \frac{5}{6}$ 2. $\frac{16}{32} = \frac{1}{2}$ 3. $\frac{21}{27} = \frac{7}{9}$ 4. $\frac{10}{15} = \frac{2}{3}$ 5. $\frac{14}{21} = \frac{2}{3}$

6. $\frac{20}{25} = \frac{4}{5}$ 7. $\frac{27}{54} = \frac{1}{2}$ 8. $\frac{6}{18} = \frac{1}{3}$ 9. $\frac{6}{8} = \frac{3}{4}$ 10. $\frac{49}{56} = \frac{7}{8}$

11. $4\frac{9}{36} = 4\frac{1}{4}$ 12. $1\frac{9}{12} = 1\frac{3}{4}$ 13. $4\frac{4}{16} = 4\frac{1}{4}$ 14. $4\frac{9}{?} = 4\frac{1}{3}$

15. $3\frac{16}{20} = 3\frac{4}{5}$ 16. $1\frac{8}{10} = 1\frac{4}{5}$ 17. $4\frac{6}{9} = 4\frac{2}{3}$ 18. $3\frac{27}{30} = 3\frac{9}{10}$

19. $5\frac{5}{40} = 5\frac{1}{8}$ 21. $2\frac{15}{18} = 2\frac{5}{6}$ 22. $3\frac{4}{8} = 3\frac{1}{2}$

11

Page 14

Name _____   Skill: Adding Fractions with the Same Denominators

Add the fractions and reduce your answer to lowest terms.

1. $\frac{3}{6} + \frac{3}{6} = \frac{5}{6}$ 2. $\frac{3}{6} + \frac{2}{6} = \frac{3}{4}$ 3. $= \frac{5}{6}$

4. $\frac{3}{9} + \frac{4}{9} = \frac{7}{9}$ 5. $\frac{5}{7} + \frac{4}{7} = 1\frac{2}{7}$ 6. $\frac{1}{3} + \frac{1}{3} = \frac{2}{3}$

7. $\frac{2}{10} + \frac{6}{10} = \frac{4}{5}$ 8. $\frac{5}{15} + \frac{7}{15} = 1$ 9. $= \frac{4}{5}$

10. $\frac{1}{6} + \frac{5}{6} = 1$ 11. $\frac{3}{8} + \frac{7}{8} = 1\frac{1}{4}$ 12. $\frac{6}{12} + \frac{4}{12} = \frac{5}{6}$

13. $\frac{5}{10} + \frac{7}{10} = 1\frac{1}{5}$ 14. $\frac{9}{18} + \frac{7}{18} = 1\frac{8}{9}$ 15. $= \frac{7}{8}$

16. $\frac{2}{4} + \frac{4}{4} = 1\frac{1}{2}$ 17. $\frac{4}{11} + \frac{9}{11} = 1\frac{3}{5}$ 18. $= 1\frac{1}{3}$

14

Page 10

Name _____   Skill: Finding the Least Common Multiple

Write the first eight multiples of each number, then write the least common multiple (LCM).

	pair of numbers	multiples	LCM
1.	4 and 6	4 = 4, 8, 12, 16, 20, 24, 28, 32 6 = 6, 12, 18, 24, 30, 36, 42, 48	12
2.	10 and 12	10 = 10, 20, 30, 40, 50, 60, 70, 80 12 = 12, 24, 36, 48, 60, 72, 84, 96	60
3.	5 and 8	5 = 5, 10, 15, 20, 25, 30, 35, 40 8 = 8, 16, 24, 32, 40, 48, 56, 64	40
4.	10 and 15	10 = 10, 20, 30, 40, 50, 60, 70, 80 15 = 15, 30, 45, 60, 75, 90, 105, 120	30
5.	4 and 8	4 = 4, 8, 12, 16, 20, 24, 28, 32 8 = 8, 16, 24, 32, 40, 48, 56, 64	8
6.	6 and 9	6 = 6, 12, 18, 24, 30, 36, 42, 48 9 = 9, 18, 27, 36, 45, 54, 63, 72	18
7.	4 and 10	4 = 4, 8, 12, 16, 20, 24, 28, 32 10 = 10, 20, 30, 40, 50, 60, 70, 80	20
8.	7 and 35	7 = 7, 14, 21, 28, 35, 42, 49, 56 35 = 35, 70, 105, 140, 175, 210, 245, 280	35
9.	3 and 4	3 = 3, 6, 9, 12, 15, 18, 21, 24 4 = 4, 8, 12, 16, 20, 24, 28, 32	12
10.	7 and 4	7 = 7, 14, 21, 28, 35, 42, 49, 56 4 = 4, 8, 12, 16, 20, 24, 28, 32	28

10

Page 13

Name _____   Skill: Changing Improper Fractions to Mixed Numbers

Change each improper fraction to a mixed number.

1. $\frac{34}{9} = 3\frac{7}{9}$ 2. $\frac{55}{7} = 7\frac{6}{7}$ 3. $\frac{51}{4} = 12\frac{3}{4}$ 4. $\frac{22}{3} = 7\frac{1}{3}$

5. $\frac{65}{8} = 8\frac{1}{8}$ 6. $\frac{85}{6} = 14\frac{1}{6}$ 7. $\frac{47}{9} = 5\frac{2}{9}$ 8. $\frac{67}{11} = 6\frac{1}{11}$

9. $\frac{25}{2} = 12\frac{1}{2}$ 10. $\frac{211}{10} = 21\frac{1}{10}$ 11. $\frac{180}{13} = 13\frac{11}{13}$ 12. $\frac{38}{9} = 4\frac{2}{9}$

13. $\frac{77}{9} = 8\frac{5}{9}$ 14. $\frac{83}{10} = 8\frac{3}{10}$ 15. $\frac{44}{15} = 2\frac{14}{15}$ 16. $\frac{143}{20} = 7\frac{3}{20}$

17. $\frac{73}{11} = 6\frac{7}{11}$ 18. $\frac{79}{9} = 8\frac{7}{9}$ 19. $\frac{47}{5} = 9\frac{2}{5}$ 20. $\frac{75}{6} = 12\frac{1}{2}$

13

Page 9

Name _____   Skill: Finding the Greatest Common Factor

List all of the factors of each pair of numbers, then give the greatest common factor (GCF).

	pair of numbers	factors	GCF
1.	6 and 10	6 = 1, 2, 3, 6 10 = 1, 2, 5, 10	2
2.	12 and 10	12 = 1, 2, 3, 4, 6, 12 10 = 1, 2, 5, 10	2
3.	20 and 30	20 = 1, 2, 4, 5, 10, 20 30 = 1, 2, 3, 5, 6, 10, 15, 30	10
4.	8 and 40	8 = 1, 2, 4, 8 40 = 1, 2, 4, 5, 8, 10, 20, 40	8
5.	18 and 8	18 = 1, 2, 3, 6, 9, 18 8 = 1, 2, 4, 8	2
6.	48 and 36	48 = 1, 2, 3, 4, 6, 8, 12, 16, 24, 48 36 = 1, 2, 3, 4, 6, 9, 12, 18, 36	12
7.	40 and 60	40 = 1, 2, 4, 5, 8, 10, 20, 40 60 = 1, 2, 3, 4, 5, 6, 10, 12, 15, 20, 30, 60	20
8.	8 and 27	8 = 1, 2, 4, 8 27 = 1, 3, 9, 27	1
9.	24 and 56	24 = 1, 2, 3, 4, 6, 8, 12, 24 56 = 1, 2, 4, 7, 8, 14, 28, 56	8
10.	36 and 54	36 = 1, 2, 3, 4, 6, 9, 12, 18, 36 54 = 1, 2, 3, 6, 9, 18, 27, 54	18

9

Page 12

Name _____   Skill: Changing Mixed Numbers to Improper Fractions

Change the mixed numbers to improper fractions.

1. $1\frac{3}{5} = \frac{8}{5}$ 2. $1\frac{1}{5} = \frac{6}{5}$ 3. $3\frac{2}{7} = \frac{23}{7}$ 4. $3\frac{2}{7} = \frac{23}{7}$

5. $6\frac{3}{18} = \frac{111}{18}$ 6. $2\frac{3}{4} = \frac{11}{4}$ 7. $5\frac{10}{15} = \frac{85}{15}$ 8. $6\frac{16}{20} = \frac{136}{20}$

9. $4\frac{1}{6} = \frac{25}{6}$ 10. $2\frac{5}{7} = \frac{19}{7}$ 11. $1\frac{4}{16} = \frac{20}{16}$ 12. $4\frac{1}{12} = \frac{16}{12}$

13. $2\frac{5}{6} = \frac{17}{6}$ 14. $4\frac{2}{5} = \frac{22}{5}$ 15. $3\frac{2}{7} = \frac{17}{7}$ 16. $4\frac{9}{15} = \frac{69}{15}$

17. $5\frac{1}{3} = \frac{16}{3}$ 18. $4\frac{3}{4} = \frac{19}{4}$ 19. $3\frac{10}{14} = \frac{52}{14}$ 20. $3\frac{4}{5} = \frac{19}{5}$

12

Answer Key

Teacher's Friend Publications ©

44

TF-1334 Sixth Grade Basic Skills
Math Drill

Answer Key

TF-1334 Sixth Grade Basic Skills
Math Drill

Page 21

Name _____

Skill: Multiplying Fractions and Whole Numbers

Multiply the fractions and reduce your answer to lowest terms.

1. $5 \times \frac{2}{3} = 3\frac{1}{3}$
2. $7 \times \frac{1}{5} = 1\frac{2}{5}$
3. $2 \times \frac{5}{8} = 1\frac{1}{4}$
4. $3 \times \frac{1}{7} = \frac{3}{7}$
5. $5 \times \frac{1}{8} = \frac{5}{8}$
6. $8 \times \frac{5}{7} = 5\frac{5}{7}$
7. $9 \times \frac{1}{3} = 3$
8. $6 \times \frac{5}{6} = 5$
9. $10 \times \frac{2}{7} = 2\frac{6}{7}$
10. $1 \times \frac{1}{2} = \frac{1}{2}$
11. $4 \times \frac{3}{5} = 2\frac{2}{5}$
12. $3 \times \frac{7}{9} = 2\frac{1}{3}$
13. $2 \times \frac{3}{8} = 3\frac{3}{8}$
14. $4 \times \frac{2}{9} = \frac{4}{9}$
15. $6 \times \frac{7}{10} = 4\frac{1}{5}$
16. $9 \times \frac{3}{8} = 3\frac{3}{8}$
17. $4 \times \frac{7}{24} = 2\frac{2}{3}$
18. $8 \times \frac{1}{6} = 1\frac{1}{3}$

21

Page 22

Name _____

Skill: Dividing Fractions

Divide the fractions and reduce your answer to lowest terms.

1. $\frac{1}{3} \div \frac{1}{6} = 2$
2. $\frac{5}{6} \div \frac{2}{3} = 1\frac{1}{4}$
3. $\frac{7}{12} \div \frac{1}{4} = 2\frac{1}{3}$
4. $\frac{1}{9} \div \frac{2}{3} = \frac{1}{6}$
5. $\frac{10}{11} \div \frac{2}{5} = 2\frac{3}{11}$
6. $\frac{3}{8} \div \frac{5}{24} = 4\frac{1}{5}$
7. $\frac{4}{5} \div \frac{7}{10} = 1\frac{1}{7}$
8. $\frac{11}{20} \div \frac{3}{4} = \frac{3}{5}$
9. $\frac{9}{20} \div \frac{3}{5} = \frac{3}{4}$
10. $\frac{9}{14} \div \frac{3}{7} = 1\frac{1}{2}$
11. $\frac{17}{20} \div \frac{3}{4} = 3\frac{2}{3}$
12. $\frac{5}{12} \div \frac{15}{24} = \frac{2}{3}$
13. $\frac{4}{5} \div \frac{1}{10} = 8$
14. $\frac{1}{6} \div \frac{7}{24} = \frac{4}{7}$
15. $\frac{15}{16} \div \frac{3}{4} = 1\frac{1}{4}$
16. $\frac{11}{18} \div \frac{2}{9} = 2\frac{3}{4}$
17. $\frac{14}{27} \div \frac{7}{9} = \frac{2}{3}$
18. $\frac{13}{30} \div \frac{1}{15} = 6\frac{1}{2}$

22

Page 23

Name _____

Skill: Dividing Fractions and Whole Numbers

Divide the fractions and whole numbers and reduce your answer to lowest terms.

1. $\frac{4}{5} \div 2 = \frac{2}{5}$
2. $9 \div \frac{9}{10} = 10$
3. $\frac{4}{7} \div 8 = \frac{1}{14}$
4. $3 \div \frac{6}{11} = 5\frac{1}{2}$
5. $15 \div 3 = 5$
7. $\frac{3}{4} \div 11 = \frac{3}{44}$
8. $12 \div \frac{3}{11} = 44$
9. $18 \div \frac{3}{5} = 30$
10. $14 \div \frac{2}{5} = 35$
11. $1 \div \frac{5}{8} = 1\frac{3}{5}$
12. $\frac{1}{8} \div 4 = \frac{1}{32}$
13. $5 \div \frac{10}{13} = 6\frac{1}{2}$
14. $9 \div \frac{6}{15} = 22\frac{1}{2}$
15. $\frac{3}{8} \div 21 = \frac{1}{56}$
16. $16 \div \frac{4}{9} = 36$
17. $\frac{7}{2} \div 10 = \frac{1}{35}$
18. $20 \div \frac{5}{9} = 36$

23

Page 24

Name _____

Skill: Dividing Mixed Numbers and Fractions

Divide the fractions and mixed numbers and reduce your answer to lowest terms.

1. $4\frac{2}{7} \div \frac{1}{4} = 17\frac{1}{7}$
2. $1\frac{3}{7} \div \frac{1}{3} = 4\frac{2}{7}$
3. $4\frac{6}{7} \div \frac{1}{3} = 14\frac{4}{7}$
4. $\frac{2}{3} \div 1\frac{7}{9} = \frac{3}{8}$
5. $\frac{1}{3} \div 1\frac{5}{6} = \frac{2}{11}$
6. $3\frac{9}{10} \div \frac{1}{6} = 23\frac{2}{5}$
7. $3\frac{7}{8} \div \frac{2}{3} = 5\frac{13}{16}$
8. $\frac{1}{3} \div 5\frac{5}{9} = \frac{3}{50}$
9. $8\frac{1}{4} \div \frac{1}{6} = 49\frac{1}{2}$
10. $\frac{3}{8} \div 5\frac{5}{6} = \frac{9}{140}$
11. $\frac{3}{4} \div 5\frac{1}{7} = \frac{7}{48}$
12. $3\frac{6}{7} \div \frac{1}{5} = 19\frac{2}{7}$

24

Page 25

Name _____

Skill: Making Fractions Equivalent

Fill in the missing part of each pair of fractions to make them equivalent.

1. $\frac{3}{4} = \frac{12}{16}$
2. $\frac{2}{3} = \frac{6}{9}$
3. $\frac{7}{15} = \frac{21}{45}$
4. $\frac{4}{5} = \frac{20}{25}$
5. $\frac{3}{8} = \frac{12}{32}$
6. $\frac{5}{9} = \frac{15}{27}$
7. $\frac{7}{8} = \frac{21}{24}$
8. $\frac{7}{12} = \frac{14}{24}$

In each row, circle the fractions that are equivalent to the first fraction.

9. $\frac{1}{3}$ — $\textcircled{\frac{3}{9}}$ $\frac{9}{10}$ $\frac{5}{15}$ $\frac{6}{17}$ $\textcircled{\frac{4}{12}}$
10. $\frac{2}{5}$ — $\textcircled{\frac{10}{25}}$ $\frac{8}{22}$ $\textcircled{\frac{2}{6}}$ $\frac{14}{35}$ $\frac{18}{30}$
11. $\frac{3}{7}$ — $\frac{24}{58}$ $\textcircled{\frac{9}{21}}$ $\frac{30}{60}$ $\textcircled{\frac{15}{35}}$ $\textcircled{\frac{24}{56}}$
12. $\frac{4}{5}$ — $\frac{12}{25}$ $\textcircled{\frac{12}{15}}$ $\frac{16}{20}$ $\textcircled{\frac{12}{15}}$ $\frac{8}{10}$
13. $\frac{7}{8}$ — $\frac{14}{16}$ $\frac{14}{16}$ $\frac{28}{32}$ $\textcircled{\frac{42}{48}}$ $\frac{49}{72}$
14. $\frac{1}{6}$ — $\frac{5}{30}$ $\textcircled{\frac{3}{18}}$ $\frac{3}{36}$ $\frac{8}{36}$ $\textcircled{\frac{10}{60}}$
15. $\frac{5}{9}$ — $\frac{25}{30}$ $\frac{15}{18}$ $\textcircled{\frac{10}{18}}$ $\frac{30}{25}$ $\frac{45}{54}$

25

Page 26

Name _____

Skill: Adding Decimals

Add the numbers.

1. $63.807 + 1.054 = 64.861$
2. $2.368 + .257 = 2.625$
3. $46.315 + 9.887 = 56.202$
4. $123.021 + 6.009 = 129.03$
5. $42.046 + .3201 = 42.3661$
6. $162.09 + 1.066 = 163.156$
7. $62.2 + .0083 = 62.2083$
8. $27.437 + 1.00215 = 28.43915$
9. $31.426 + 27.2 = 58.626$
10. $.045 + 62.7 = 62.745$
11. $3,214.6 + 2.504 = 3217.104$
12. $10.05 + 312.625 = 322.675$
13. $.14 + .005 = 14.005$
14. $.5 + 12.761 = 13.261$
15. $99.9 + 1.99 = 101.89$
16. $5.73 + 1.0024 = 6.7324$
17. $3.5 + 4.5 = 8$
18. $.059 + 22.6 = 22.659$
19. $86.982 + .404 = 87.386$
20. $5.711 + 142.08 = 147.791$

26

Answer Key

Skill: Dividing Decimals

Divide the numbers.

1. $6\overline{)42.1}$ = 7.017
2. $3\overline{)33.9}$ = 11.3
3. $2\overline{)8.4}$ = 4.2
4. $9\overline{)5.15}$ = .572
5. $4\overline{)1.85}$ = .4625
6. $3\overline{)5.41}$ = 1.803
7. $6\overline{)5.81}$ = .9683
8. $2\overline{).36}$ = .18

9. 8 ÷ 3.91 = 2.046
10. 3 ÷ 13.07 = .2295
11. 8 ÷ 58.6 = .1365
12. 5 ÷ 5.22 = .9578
13. 3 ÷ 10.6 = .283
14. 8 ÷ 3.152 = 2.538
15. 6 ÷ 5.87 = 1.022
16. 6 ÷ 36.12 = .1661
17. 12 ÷ 122.2 = .0982
18. 42 ÷ 29.34 = 1.5945
19. 64 ÷ 125.6 = .5095
20. 21 ÷ 5.06 = 4.1502

29

Page 29

Skill: Multiplying Decimals

Multiply the numbers.

1. 42.7 x 6.809 = 290.7443
2. 13.6 x 22.7 = 308.72
3. 40.301 x 6.07 = 244.62707
4. 99.12 x 8.6 = 852.432
5. 4.23 x 6.5 = 27.495
6. 1.5 x 6.07 = 9.105
7. 13.8 x 5.6 = 77.28
8. .012 x .75 = .009

9. 6.49 x 3.21 = 20.8329
10. .481 x 39.5 = 18.9995
11. 87.4 x .51 = 44.574
12. 6.35 x 2.9 = 18.415
13. 27.6 x .17 = 4.692
14. 45.1 x .35 = 15.785
15. 4.13 x .35 = 1.4455
16. 6.21 x 2.7 = 16.767
17. 28.2 x .38 = 10.716
18. 1.2 x 44 = 52.8
19. 2.57 x 53.5 = 137.495
20. 5.12 x 2.83 = 14.4896

28

Page 28

Skill: Subtracting Decimals

Subtract the numbers.

1. 30.62 - 15.01 = 15.61
2. 721.83 - .42 = 721.41
3. 39.628 - 11.64 = 27.988
4. 26.02 - 3.14 = 22.88
5. 17.602 - 4.98 = 12.622
6. 37.509 - 24.7 = 12.809
7. 225.99 - .027 = 225.963
8. 241.62 - 80.4 = 161.22

9. 42.6 - 24.062 = 18.538
10. 67.502 - 25.4 = 42.102
11. 396.09 - 71.225 = 324.865
12. 42.65 - 27.109 = 15.541
13. 584.6 - .0047 = 584.5953
14. 17.401 - 3.52 = 13.881
15. 471.55 - 32.0627 = 439.4873
16. 12.94 - 9.062 = 3.878
17. 47.02 - 13.088 = 33.932
18. 88.65 - 17.92 = 70.73
19. 4.003 - 3.4 = .603
20. 22.6 - 9.332 = 13.268

27

Page 27

Skill: Changing Percentages to Fractions

Change each percentage to a fraction.

1. 1% = 1/100
2. 224% = 2 6/25
3. 14% = 7/50
4. 30% = 3/10
5. 18% = 9/50
6. 22% = 11/50
7. 85% = 17/20
8. 2% = 1/50
9. 115% = 1 3/20
10. 95% = 95/100
11. 20% = 1/5
12. 40% = 2/5
13. 100% = 1 1/1
14. 156% = 1 14/25
15. 12% = 3/25
16. 4% = 1/25
17. 11% = 11/100
18. 145% = 1 9/20
19. 42% = 21/50
20. 78% = 39/50

32

Page 32

Skill: Changing Decimals to Fractions

Change each decimal to a fraction or mixed number.

1. .16 = 4/25
2. 2.07 = 2 7/100
3. 2.7 = 2 7/10
4. .87 = 87/100
5. 6.5 = 6 1/2
6. 5.9 = 5 9/10
7. 3.75 = 3 3/4
8. 4.125 = 4 1/8
9. 1.4 = 1 2/5
10. .6 = 3/5
11. 4.2 = 4 1/5
12. 6.8 = 6 4/5
13. .375 = 3/8
14. .35 = 7/20
15. .62 = 31/50
16. .16 = 4/25
17. 2.02 = 2 1/50
18. .05 = 1/20
19. .18 = 9/50
20. 3.03 = 3 3/100

31

Page 31

Skill: Changing Fractions and Mixed Numbers to Decimals

Change the fractions or mixed numbers to decimals.

1. 7/20 = .35
2. 3/4 = .75
3. 1/2 = .5
4. 9/10 = .9
5. 3/8 = .375
6. 2 5/8 = 2.625
7. 4 3/10 = 4.3
8. 7/10 = .7
9. 9/20 = .45
10. 3 2/5 = 3.4
11. 6 4/25 = 6.16
12. 3/40 = .075
13. 7/50 = .14
14. 19/20 = .95
15. 1/8 = .125
16. 2 1/5 = 2.2
17. 3/5 = .6
18. 6 1/4 = 6.25
19. 11/20 = .55
20. 4/5 = .8

30

Page 30

Answer Key

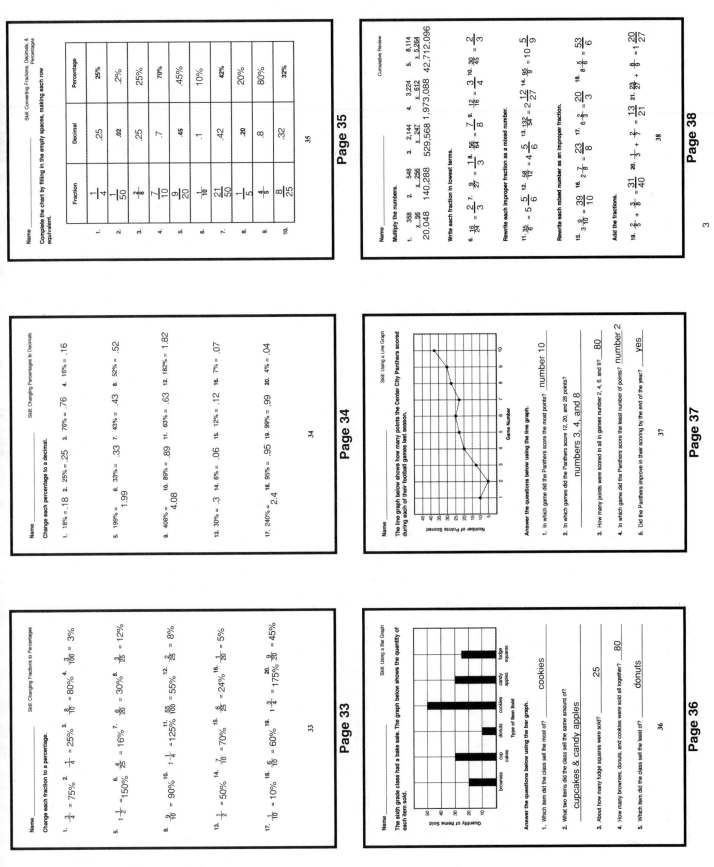

Page 35

Name _____

Skill: Converting Fractions, Decimals, & Percentages

Complete the chart by filling in the empty spaces, making each row equivalent.

	Fraction	Decimal	Percentage
1.	$\frac{1}{4}$	.25	25%
2.	$\frac{1}{50}$	.02	.2%
3.	$\frac{2}{8}$	.25	25%
4.	$\frac{7}{10}$	.7	70%
5.	$\frac{9}{20}$	.45	.45%
6.	$\frac{1}{10}$	.1	10%
7.	$\frac{21}{50}$	.42	42%
8.	$\frac{1}{5}$	.20	20%
9.	$\frac{4}{5}$	.8	80%
10.	$\frac{8}{25}$	.32	32%

35

Page 38

Name _____

Skill: Cumulative Review

Multiply the numbers.

1. 358 × 56 = 20,048
2. 548 × 256 = 140,288
3. 2,144 × 247 = 529,568
4. 3,224 × 612 = 1,973,088
5. 8,114 × 5,264 = 42,712,096

Write each fraction in lowest terms.

6. $\frac{16}{24} = \frac{2}{3}$
7. $\frac{9}{27} = \frac{1}{3}$
8. $\frac{56}{64} = \frac{7}{8}$
9. $\frac{12}{16} = \frac{3}{4}$
10. $\frac{30}{45} = \frac{2}{3}$

Rewrite each improper fraction as a mixed number.

11. $\frac{35}{6} = 5\frac{5}{6}$
12. $\frac{58}{12} = 4\frac{5}{6}$
13. $\frac{132}{54} = 2\frac{12}{27}$
14. $\frac{95}{9} = 10\frac{5}{9}$

Rewrite each mixed number as an improper fraction.

15. $3\frac{9}{10} = \frac{39}{10}$
16. $2\frac{7}{8} = \frac{23}{8}$
17. $6\frac{2}{3} = \frac{20}{3}$
18. $8\frac{5}{6} = \frac{53}{6}$

Add the fractions.

19. $\frac{2}{5} + \frac{3}{8} = \frac{31}{40}$
20. $\frac{1}{3} + \frac{7}{7} = \frac{13}{21}$
21. $\frac{23}{27} + \frac{8}{9} = 1\frac{20}{27}$

3

Page 34

Name _____

Skill: Changing Percentages to Decimals

Change each percentage to a decimal.

1. 18% = .18
2. 25% = .25
3. 76% = .76
4. 16% = .16
5. 199% = 1.99
6. 33% = .33
7. 43% = .43
8. 52% = .52
9. 408% = 4.08
10. 89% = .89
11. 63% = .63
12. 182% = 1.82
13. 30% = .3
14. 6% = .06
15. 12% = .12
16. 7% = .07
17. 240% = 2.4
18. 95% = .95
19. 99% = .99
20. 4% = .04

34

Page 37

Name _____

Skill: Using a Line Graph

The line graph below shows how many points the Center City Panthers scored during each of their football games last season.

Answer the questions below using the line graph.

1. In which game did the Panthers score the most points? **number 10**

2. In which games did the Panthers score 12, 20, and 28 points? **numbers 3, 4, and 8**

3. How many points were scored in all in games number 2, 4, 6, and 9? **80**

4. In which game did the Panthers score the least number of points? **number 2**

5. Did the Panthers improve in their scoring by the end of the year? **yes**

37

Page 33

Name _____

Skill: Changing Fractions to Percentages

Change each fraction to a percentage.

1. $\frac{3}{4} = 75\%$
2. $\frac{1}{4} = 25\%$
3. $\frac{8}{10} = 80\%$
4. $\frac{3}{100} = 3\%$
5. $1\frac{1}{2} = 150\%$
6. $\frac{4}{25} = 16\%$
7. $\frac{6}{20} = 30\%$
8. $\frac{3}{25} = 12\%$
9. $\frac{9}{10} = 90\%$
10. $1\frac{1}{4} = 125\%$
11. $\frac{55}{100} = 55\%$
12. $\frac{2}{25} = 8\%$
13. $\frac{1}{2} = 50\%$
14. $\frac{7}{10} = 70\%$
15. $\frac{6}{25} = 24\%$
16. $\frac{1}{20} = 5\%$
17. $\frac{1}{10} = 10\%$
18. $\frac{6}{10} = 60\%$
19. $1\frac{3}{4} = 175\%$
20. $\frac{9}{20} = 45\%$

33

Page 36

Name _____

Skill: Using a Bar Graph

The sixth grade class had a bake sale. The graph below shows the quantity of each item sold.

Answer the questions below using the bar graph.

1. Which item did the class sell the most of? **cookies**

2. What two items did the class sell the same amount of? **cupcakes & candy apples**

3. About how many fudge squares were sold? **25**

4. How many brownies, donuts, and cookies were sold all together? **80**

5. Which item did the class sell the least? **donuts**

36

Answer Key

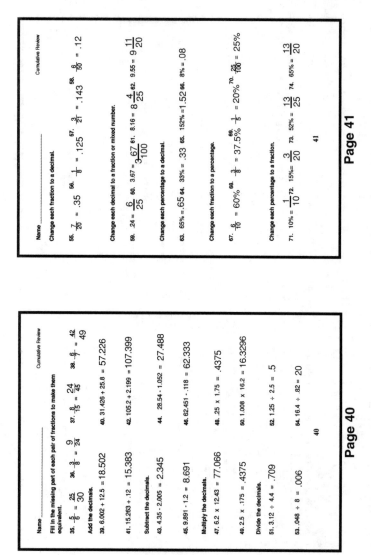

Page 39

Name _____ Cumulative Review

Add the mixed numbers.

22. $4\frac{2}{7} + 3\frac{11}{14} = 8\frac{1}{14}$ 23. $3\frac{3}{5} + 4\frac{1}{8} = 7\frac{29}{40}$

Subtract the fractions.

24. $\frac{5}{6} - \frac{1}{3} = \frac{1}{2}$ 25. $\frac{7}{9} - \frac{3}{8} = \frac{29}{72}$ 26. $\frac{9}{10} - \frac{3}{5} = \frac{3}{10}$

Subtract the mixed numbers.

27. $5\frac{2}{3} - 4\frac{4}{9} = 1\frac{4}{9}$ 28. $8\frac{5}{6} - 5\frac{3}{5} = 3\frac{7}{30}$

Multiply the fractions.

29. $\frac{2}{3} \times \frac{1}{8} = \frac{1}{12}$ 30. $\frac{10}{15} \times \frac{2}{13} = \frac{2}{13}$ 31. $\frac{4}{7} \times \frac{14}{15} = \frac{8}{15}$

Divide the fractions.

32. $\frac{10}{11} \div \frac{15}{22} = 1\frac{1}{3}$ 33. $\frac{3}{4} \div \frac{15}{16} = \frac{4}{5}$ 34. $\frac{9}{10} \div \frac{2}{3} = 1\frac{7}{20}$

39

Page 40

Name _____ Cumulative Review

Fill in the missing part of each pair of fractions to make them equivalent.

35. $\frac{5}{6} = \frac{25}{30}$ 36. $\frac{3}{8} = \frac{9}{24}$ 37. $\frac{8}{15} = \frac{24}{45}$ 38. $\frac{6}{7} = \frac{42}{49}$

Add the decimals.

39. $6.002 + 12.5 = 18.502$ 40. $31.426 + 25.8 = 57.226$

41. $15.263 + .12 = 15.383$ 42. $105.2 + 2.199 = 107.399$

Subtract the decimals.

43. $4.35 - 2.005 = 2.345$ 44. $28.54 - 1.052 = 27.488$

45. $9.891 - 1.2 = 8.691$ 46. $62.451 - .118 = 62.333$

Multiply the decimals.

47. $6.2 \times 12.43 = 77.066$ 48. $.25 \times 1.75 = .4375$

49. $2.5 \times .175 = .4375$ 50. $1.008 \times 16.2 = 16.3296$

Divide the decimals.

51. $3.12 \div 4.4 = .709$ 52. $1.25 \div 2.5 = .5$

53. $.048 \div 8 = .006$ 54. $16.4 \div .82 = 20$

40

Page 41

Name _____ Cumulative Review

Change each fraction to a decimal.

55. $\frac{7}{20} = .35$ 56. $\frac{1}{8} = .125$ 57. $\frac{3}{21} = .143$ 58. $\frac{6}{50} = .12$

Change each decimal to a fraction or mixed number.

59. $.24 = \frac{6}{25}$ 60. $3.67 = 3\frac{67}{100}$ 61. $8.16 = 8\frac{4}{25}$ 62. $9.55 = 9\frac{11}{20}$

Change each percentage to a decimal.

63. $65\% = .65$ 64. $33\% = .33$ 65. $152\% = 1.52$ 66. $8\% = .08$

Change each fraction to a percentage.

67. $\frac{6}{10} = 60\%$ 68. $\frac{3}{8} = 37.5\%$ 69. $\frac{1}{5} = 20\%$ 70. $\frac{25}{100} = 25\%$

Change each percentage to a fraction.

71. $10\% = \frac{1}{10}$ 72. $15\% = \frac{3}{20}$ 73. $52\% = \frac{13}{25}$ 74. $65\% = \frac{13}{20}$

41